THE BLACK
ORDER BRIGADE

Enki Bilal / Pierre Christin

THE BLACK
ORDER BRIGADE

Humanoids Publishing ™

Atadell

Christian Avidsen

Donahue

Gian Carlo
Di Manno

Felipe Castejon

Paul-Marie
Barsac

Ephraïm Katz

Hans Kessler

Pavel Stransky

Jefferson B. Pritchard

Maria Wizniewska

"THE SLEEP OF REASON BREEDS MONSTERS."
GOYA

http://www.humanoids-publishing.com

THE BLACK ORDER BRIGADE

TRANSLATION BY JUSTIN KELLY

English language edition © 2000 Humanoids Inc. Los Angeles, CA, USA.
Original French edition : Les Phalanges de l'Ordre Noir
© 1994 Les Humanoïdes Associés S.A. Geneva, Switzerland.
All rights reserved.

Humanoids Publishing
PO Box 931658
Hollywood, CA 90093

Printed in Belgium. Bound in France.

ISBN : 0 9672401 8 2
43 4952 8

Humanoids Publishing™ and the Humanoids Publishing logo are trademarks of
Les Humanoïdes Associés S.A., Geneva (Switzerland), registered in various categories and countries.
Humanoids Publishing, a division of Humanoids Group.

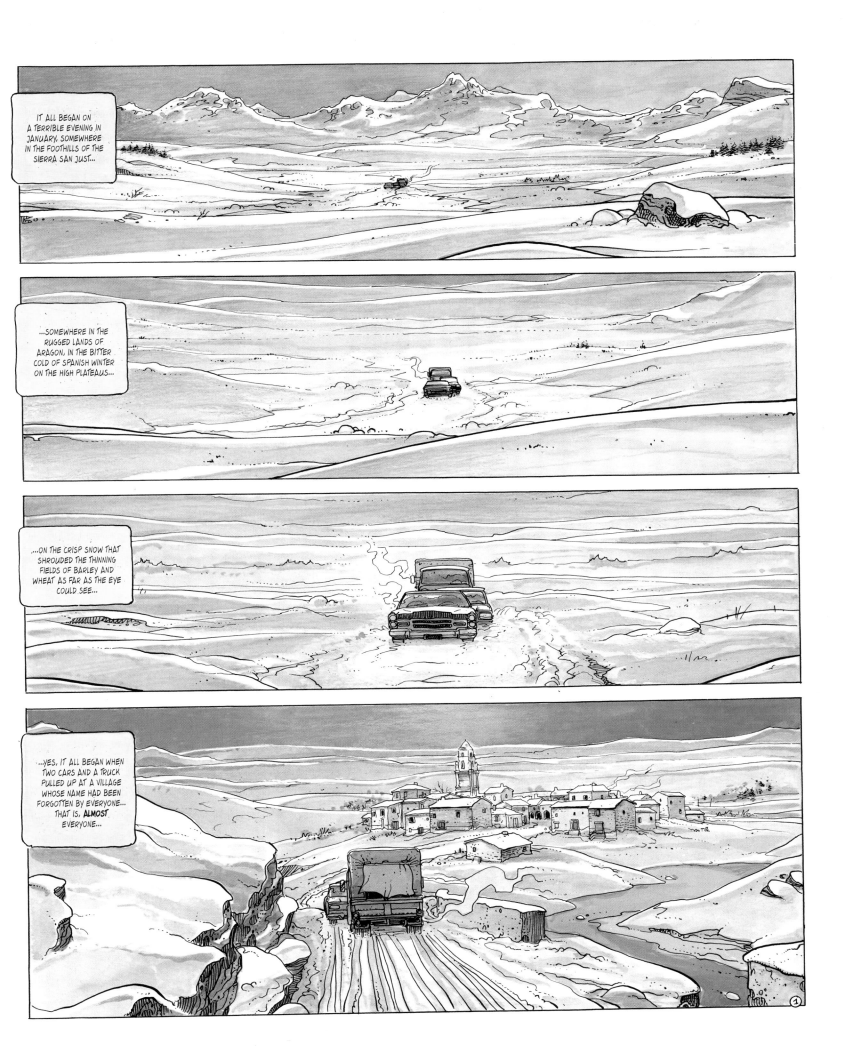

IT ALL BEGAN ON A TERRIBLE EVENING IN JANUARY, SOMEWHERE IN THE FOOTHILLS OF THE SIERRA SAN JUST...

...SOMEWHERE IN THE RUGGED LANDS OF ARAGON, IN THE BITTER COLD OF SPANISH WINTER ON THE HIGH PLATEAUS...

...ON THE CRISP SNOW THAT SHROUDED THE THINNING FIELDS OF BARLEY AND WHEAT AS FAR AS THE EYE COULD SEE...

...YES, IT ALL BEGAN WHEN TWO CARS AND A TRUCK PULLED UP AT A VILLAGE WHOSE NAME HAD BEEN FORGOTTEN BY EVERYONE... THAT IS, **ALMOST** EVERYONE...

1

¡ HAN RE-
GRESADO!

YOU'RE RIGHT, OLD WOMAN,
WE HAVE COME BACK!...
BUT THIS TIME...

PANG

...I WON'T MISS...

OUTSIDE,
YOU COMMIE
MAYOR!

ALL CLEANED
UP?

TOO EASY...

9

GT 027 REUTER 16:42
MADRID JANUARY 12
TERRORISM. ARAGON VILLAGE WIPED OFF THE MAP.

THE TINY VILLAGE OF NIEVES (POP. 72) WAS COMPLETELY DESTROYED AND ITS ENTIRE POPULATION MASSACRED ON JANUARY 11 AROUND 19.00 (LOCAL TIME). A TERRORIST UNIT BURST INTO THE VILLAGE AND COMMENCED A SYSTEMATIC RAID UPON THE INHABITANTS, INCLUDING WOMEN AND CHILDREN, WHO WERE SLAUGHTERED WITH MACHINE PISTOLS AND HANDGUNS.
NEXT, THE INVADERS SET FIRE TO THE VILLAGE, WHICH WAS COMPLETELY DESTROYED. THE NEWS WAS DISCOVERED ON JANUARY 12 ONLY BECAUSE OF THE ISOLATION OF THE VILLAGE. THE FIRST RESCUE TEAMS APPARENTLY FOUND NO SURVIVORS.

...TER 16:53
...VILLAGE (CONTD)
...SENT TO A MADRID RADIO STATION CLAIMING
...TY FOR THE ATTACK. THE COMPLETE TEXT HAS NOT YET
...UBLIC. HOWEVER, THE TEXT WAS SENT BY "THE BLACK
...ADE". IT INVOKES "GOOD CHRISTIAN VALUES" AND
...THE COMPLETE DESTRUCTION OF NIEVES AS "AN EXAMPLE".
...UNITIVE INCIDENTS ARE TO FOLLOW.
...THAT THE VILLAGE WAS ONE OF THE PRIMARY

WOMEN AND CHILDREN, WHO WERE SLAUGHTERED WITH MACHINE PISTOLS AND HANDGUNS.
NEXT, THE INVADERS SET FIRE TO THE VILLAGE, WHICH WAS COMPLETELY DESTROYED. THE NEWS WAS DISCOVERED ON JANUARY 12 ONLY BECAUSE OF THE ISOLATION OF THE VILLAGE. THE FIRST RESCUE TEAMS APPARENTLY FOUND NO SURVIVORS.

GT 028 REUTER 16:53
ARAGON VILLAGE (CONTD)
A RECORDED STATEMENT WAS SENT TO A MADRID RADIO STATION CLAIMING RESPONSIBILITY FOR THE ATTACK. THE COMPLETE TEXT HAS NOT YET BEEN MADE PUBLIC. HOWEVER, THE TEXT WAS SENT BY "THE BLACK ORDER BRIGADE". IT INVOKES "GOOD CHRISTIAN VALUES" AND REFERS TO THE COMPLETE DESTRUCTION OF NIEVES AS "AN EXAMPLE". FURTHER PUNITIVE INCIDENTS ARE TO FOLLOW.
ONE IS REMINDED MOREOVER THAT THE VILLAGE WAS ONE OF THE PRIMARY ZONES OF CONFLICT BETWEEN THE REPUBLICANS AND THE FRANQUISTAS THROUGHOUT THE WINTER OF 1938, IN THE SPANISH CIVIL WAR, BEFORE IT WAS TAKEN BY GEN. CAUDILLO'S TROOPS.
HOWEVER, DURING THE LAST ELECTION HELD IN THIS LONG-TIME SYMBOLIC VILLAGE, THE VOTE SWUNG WILDLY TO THE LEFT. THE NEW MAYOR WAS ONE OF THE VICTIMS OF THE ATTACK.

NOTE TO EDITORIAL STAFF: A SYNTHESIS WILL BE TRANSMITTED AT APPROX. 18:00 HRS.

5

WELL, MR. PRITCHARD? WHAT DO YOU THINK?

WHAT DO I THINK? WELL...

SIR! OUR SPANISH CORRESPONDENT HAS JUST PHONED FROM ZARAGOZA...

AH, MY GOOD FRIEND ATADELL... READ ME BACK HIS COPY, WILL YOU...

ATTACK CLAIMED BY THE BLACK ORDER BRIGADE. AN UNOFFICIAL BUT DEFINITIVE LIST HAS BEEN CIRCULATED... COMPRISES THE NAMES OF THOSE INVOLVED IN ARAGON... HERE THEY ARE:

MIGUEL VALIÑO, LIEUTENANT, KNOWN FOR HIS RUTHLESSNESS DURING THE SUPPRESSION OF ASTURIAN MINERS DURING THE REPUBLIC, AND PROMOTED TO GENERAL UNDER FRANCO.

SAINTS ALIVE! VALIÑO!

ETTORE PISCIOTTA, FORMER TANK COMMANDER SENT BY MUSSOLINI IN SUPPORT OF FRANCO... JOAQUIN DE VALLELLANO, FALLEN ARISTOCRAT, GUERRILLA MEMBER OF "CHRIST THE KING"...

SAINTS ALIVE! PISCIOTTA, VALLELLANO!

HANS HEINKEL, FORMERLY OF THE CONDOR LEGION, SENT INTO BATTLE BY HITLER... DU BUSQUET, FRENCH, LATER REPORTED AT VICHY, IN THE OAS...

SAINTS -! BUT THEY'RE ALL THERE!!!

...JAVIER, FORMERLY OF THE LEGION AZUL, LENT TO GERMANY BY SPAIN DURING WORLD WAR II... COLPIN, FRENCH MERCENARY RECENTLY RETURNED FROM MAURITANIA... KUYPER, A BELGIAN ACCUSED OF REXISM WHO TOOK REFUGE IN MADRID... AND AN ITALIAN, A GREEK, AND A SPANIARD, ALL UNIDENTIFIED...

ALL OF THEM, I TELL YOU!

WHAT DO YOU MEAN "ALL"?

TAKE A LOOK AT THESE PHOTOS, KID. I WASN'T EVER GOING TO SHOW THEM TO YOU... THIS ONE IS NIEVES! OR WAS, I SHOULD SAY. ME AND MY BUDDIES IN THE 15TH INTERNATIONAL BRIGADE FOUGHT FOR WEEKS AND WEEKS IN THAT TOWN AGAINST THOSE BASTARDS WHOSE NAMES YOU JUST HEARD...

IT WAS WHEN THE REPUBLIC WAS STARTING TO BREAK UP... THE COLD WAS AWFUL. WE TOOK THE VILLAGE. THEN LOST IT. THEN TOOK IT AGAIN. THEN LOST IT AGAIN... HUNDREDS KILLED ON BOTH SIDES... IT WAS TERRIBLE...

THAT'S THEM, HIGH UP ON THE HILL...

AND THAT'S US...

IT LOOKS LIKE YOU WERE WEARING FUNNY CLOTHES, EVEN FOR A VOLUNTEER BRIGADE...

HMPH... NO MORE UNIFORMS, NO MORE GUNS, NOTHING... WE STOLE SUITS AND WOOLEN JACKETS FROM THE SHOPS IN TERUEL, AND FOUGHT THEM OFF WITH BOTTLES OF NITROGLYCERINE...

AND THEM?

WELL, IN THE END, THEY WON. MEANWHILE WE, ABANDONED BY THE SOVIETS, BY THE FRENCH, BY EVERYONE, HAD TO FIND OUR WAY BACK TO BARCELONA TO BE REPATRIATED...

...EXCEPT THAT HISTORY CONTINUED ITS MARCH, AND NOW THOSE OLD LUNATICS SENSE THAT THE TIMES ARE CHANGING... AND SO...

AND SO YOU HAVE ONE HELL OF A STORY THERE, MR. PRITCHARD!

YOU SHOULD SEE MR. DUNCAN ABOUT IT...

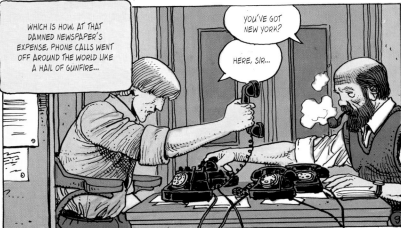

THE FIRST ONE TO SAY YES WAS **DONAHUE**, FROM HIS GRIMY OFFICE IN THE BRONX...

HELLO, IT'S PRITCHARD...

PRITCHARD!!!

HOLY SMOKE, I NEVER WOULD HAVE GUESSED! WHAT'S...

ALWAYS READY FOR A BIT OF EXCITEMENT, DONAHUE. AND DOUBTLESSLY TIRED OF PLAYING THE BOSS IN THE BUTCHER'S UNION...

HANG ON, I'LL EXPLAIN...

I'M LISTENING, PAL...

SLIGHTLY CORRUPT, HIS UNION, BUT POWERFUL... AND RICH! DONAHUE PROMISED TO TAP INTO THEIR RESERVES TO FUND OUR EXPEDITION...

OK?

OK!

AFTERWARDS, IT WAS **BARSAC'S** TURN... FORMERLY A HIGH-RANKING FRENCH OFFICER, NOW CONVERTED TO PACIFISM...

GETTING HIM TO AGREE WASN'T EASY. BUT BARSAC WAS A MAN OF LOYALTY. ISOLATED IN HIS COUNTRY HOME, HE HESITATED AT FIRST, THEN ACCEPTED...

I COULDN'T REACH **AVIDSEN** AT HIS MINISTRY. AN EVENING RECEPTION IN ONE OF THE SALONS OF COPENHAGEN. AVIDSEN, A SOCIAL DEMOCRAT, WITH A GLOBAL OUTLOOK...

...BUT ALSO AN ADVENTURER AND A GAMBLER BENEATH HIS REFINED VENEER. HE WAS ALMOST RELIEVED TO JOIN IN. HE COULD WELL HAVE BEEN FED UP WITH PLAYING MINISTERS...

NO PROBLEM WITH **DI MANNO**. ALTHOUGH THE LINE TO NAPLES WAS BAD, HE UNDERSTOOD IMMEDIATELY...

HE FAILED IN HIS CAREER AS A JUDGE, DI MANNO. TOO INDEPENDENT, ALWAYS GETTING INTO TROUBLE WITH BOTH THE LEFT AND THE RIGHT. BUT HE BELIEVED IN JUSTICE...

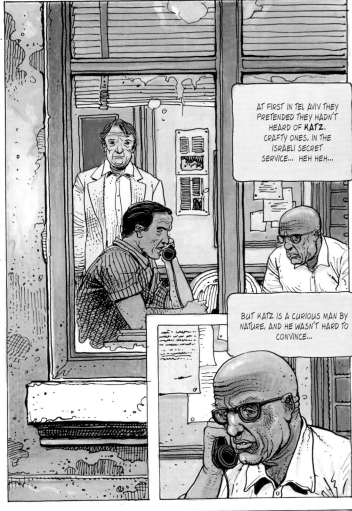

AT FIRST IN TEL AVIV THEY PRETENDED THEY HADN'T HEARD OF **KATZ**. CRAFTY ONES, IN THE ISRAELI SECRET SERVICE... HEH HEH...

BUT KATZ IS A CURIOUS MAN BY NATURE, AND HE WASN'T HARD TO CONVINCE...

...AND NEITHER WAS **STRANSKY**, FORMER COMMUNIST, FORMER ENGINEER, FORMER CZECH CITIZEN. HE'S BEEN IN EXILE IN SWITZERLAND SINCE THE 'PRAGUE SPRING'.

...AND NEITHER WAS **MARIA WIZNIEWSKA**, WHO HAD BECOME AN AUTHOR OF CHILDREN'S BOOKS IN WARSAW, BUT WHO HAD NEVER FORGOTTEN HER NIGHTS IN BARCELONA...

...AND NEITHER WAS **KESSLER**. THE GOOD PROFESSOR ALWAYS FOUND UNIVERSITIES ANNOYING, EVEN IN HEIDELBERG. ESPECIALLY SINCE HE'D BEEN UNDER THE THREAT OF OFFICIAL SANCTION ON THE CHARGE OF "INCITING ANARCHY"...

THE ONLY ONE TO SAY NO WAS THAT BASTARD **RATCLIFF**, NOW BECOME A SUCCESSFUL SCREENWRITER IN HOLLYWOOD. HOPE HE ROTS IN HIS NEO-GOTHIC BEVERLY HILLS MANSION...

AS FOR **O'ROURKE**, IT WAS HIS DAUGHTER WHO ANSWERED, TO SAY THAT HE WAS DYING. A STRAY SHOT DURING A RIOT ONE EVENING IN BELFAST. HE WHO HAD ESCAPED SO MANY BULLETS HEADED FOR HIS GENEROUS GUT...

THAT LEFT ONLY CASTEJON. A STRANGE PRIEST, **CASTEJON**. BUT HE KNEW THE BASQUE COUNTRY LIKE THE BACK OF HIS HAND...

WATCH OUT! THE FRONTIERS ARE VERY WELL-PATROLLED THESE DAYS! AND ALTHOUGH SOME OLD MEMBERS OF OUR BRIGADE HAVE LONG BEEN FORGOTTEN, THAT ISN'T THE CASE FOR ALL OF US...

WHICH MEANS...?

HE WAS THE ONE TO SET UP THE PLANS FOR OUR INGRESS. AND IF CASTEJON HADN'T ENTERED THE LORD'S SERVICE, HE WOULD HAVE ENDED UP A HIRED KILLER OR A GENERAL IN SOME ARMY...

WHICH MEANS YOU'LL RENDEZVOUS IN FRANCE, WHERE I'LL HAVE A FRIEND MEET YOU. WE'LL MEET SOMEWHERE ON THE PAMPLONA ROAD, IN THE MOUNTAINS...

IT TOOK ONE LAST CALL TO EXPLAIN EVERYTHING TO **ATADELL**, ALSO AN OLD MEMBER OF OUR BRIGADE IN NIEVES. NOW ALL WAS READY...

IT WAS A STRANGE FEELING... AND IT WAS GOING TO BE A STRANGE PHONE BILL FOR THE PAPER... BUT THE DIE HAD BEEN CAST... WELL AND TRULY CAST...

IT WAS IN A MOUNTAIN VILLAGE, BEHIND **ST JEAN-DE-LUZ**, THAT THE BIG REUNION TOOK PLACE A COUPLE OF DAYS LATER...

...FORTY YEARS AFTER OUR BRIGADE WAS DISBANDED IN 1938!

STRANSKY!!! YOU DIRTY OLD STALINIST!!!

KATZ!!! YOU OLD ZIONIST SCOUNDREL!!!

FORTY YEARS IN WHICH MOST OF US REUNITING IN THE DISCREET BACK ROOM HAD NOT SEEN EACH OTHER...

DARLING MARIA! YOU ARE TRULY RAVISHING!

DEAR BARSAC! STILL SUCH A GENTLEMAN...

IN THIS CASE, FORTY YEARS WAS A LONG TIME...

HOW'S MY OLD FRIEND THE MINISTER?

AND HOW'S MY OLD FRIEND THE PROFESSOR?

AND WHAT'S MORE, IT WAS A STRANGE COLLECTION OF ASTHMATICS, RHEUMATICS, ARTHRITICS, OUR OLD FLESH SWOLLEN BY CHOLESTEROL...

LOOKS LIKE THE UNION GIVES YOU PLENTY TO EAT!

AND YOU, IS LA MAMMA STILL LOOKING AFTER YOU?

BUT STILL, WE WEREN'T A BUNCH OF OLD SENILES YET... IN THE END, IT WAS A GOOD PARTY. IT ALMOST MADE US THINK THAT WE WERE YOUNG AGAIN...

HELLO EVERYONE!

HEY, THERE'S PRITCHARD!...

A TOAST!!!

WE DESCENDED THROUGH THE IMMENSE OAK FOREST IN ABSOLUTE SILENCE. THE ONLY SOUND WAS THE SNOW CRUNCHING UNDER OUR WEARY FEET...

WE HAD ALL HEARD THE GUNSHOTS, AND THE AVALANCHE, BUT NONE OF US SAID ANYTHING...

CASTEJON ARRIVED AT THE FARMHOUSE JUST BEFORE DAWN. AT FIRST GLANCE, HE KNEW THAT ALREADY ONE OF US WAS MISSING...

ATCHOO!

YOU'LL RIDE IN THERE TILL WE GET TO THE CHURCH! LET'S GO, COMPAÑEROS! THIS AREA IS HEAVILY GUARDED, BUT WE'LL GET THROUGH...

INDEED, WE GOT THROUGH. CASTEJON HAD CHARTERED AN AGELESS OLD BUS UNDER THE PRETENSE OF ARRANGING A PILGRIMAGE TO CATALONIA...

RATTLING ALONG THE DESERTED ROADS TOWARDS ZARAGOZA, AMONG BLACK-CLAD WOMEN EATING CHORIZO, WE ALL SAT THINKING, PERHAPS ABOUT DONAHUE...

...AND PERHAPS ABOUT DEATH ITSELF AS PEOPLE DO WHEN THEY AGE, KNOWING IT AWAITS THEM, INSIDIOUS, YET AT THE SAME TIME FAMILIAR...

ATCHOOO!

AND PERHAPS SOME OF THE OTHERS WERE ALSO THINKING ABOUT ATADELL, AND THE RENDEZVOUS THAT HAD BEEN PLANNED IN THE SUBURBS OF BARCELONA...

EXCEPT THAT THE RENDEZVOUS WAS NEVER TO TAKE PLACE... BECAUSE AFTER WE HAD DROPPED OFF CASTEJON'S FLOCK AT THE SAGRADA FAMILIA...

21

...AFTER WE HAD TRAVERSED THE CITY'S LONG AVENUES, WHICH BROUGHT BACK SO MANY MEMORIES FOR THOSE WHO HAD PATROLLED THEM IN ARMS SO MANY YEARS AGO...

IS THIS IT?

WHAT'S HAPPENING?

...DON'T KNOW...

HOW MUCH?

85 PESETAS, SEÑOR.

DIDN'T YOU HEAR IT ON THE RADIO?

THERE WAS A MASSIVE EXPLOSION!

SEEMS THE PLACE WAS FILLED WITH OLD CRACKPOTS... ANARCHISTS, FROM THE OLD **CONFEDERACIÓN NACIONAL DEL TRABAJO**...

TROTSKYISTS FROM THE **POUM**...

ALL THESE BULLSHIT UNDERGROUND ACTIVITIES FROM ANOTHER AGE, I DON'T SEE WHAT THEY'RE GOOD FOR...

THEY'RE GOOD FOR KNOCKING BACK DEMOCRATIC PROGRESS, THAT'S WHAT...

AND WHAT ABOUT THAT BLACK ORDER BRIGADE THAT CLAIMED THE ATTACK? THERE'S ANOTHER INTERESTING BUNCH...

JUST ANOTHER TYPE OF NUTCASE!

THEY'RE CERTAINLY NO BETTER...

IT'S ALL JUST OLD NEWS!

A LOT WORSE, YOU MEAN...

GOOD GRIEF! ALREADY TWO OF US ARE DEAD... AND WE DON'T KNOW ANYTHING ABOUT WHAT'S REALLY GOING ON...

ATADELL HAD PHONED TO TELL ME HE WAS HOPING TO GET SOME INFORMATION THERE, BECAUSE HE'D HEARD THE BLACK ORDER WAS PLANNING SOMETHING IN BARCELONA...

LET'S GET OUT OF HERE!

DID YOU HEAR WHAT THEY WERE SAYING?

YES... I FOUND IT ALL VERY UPSETTING... FOR US AS WELL AS THE OTHERS, I MEAN...

POOR ATADELL... LOOKS LIKE HE GOT HIS INFORMATION AFTER ALL...

TOO MUCH OF IT, OR NOT ENOUGH! THE INFORMATION GAME ISN'T FORGIVING OF THOSE KINDS OF MISTAKES, TAKE IT FROM A SPECIALIST...

AH, THOSE BASTARDS!

YES... THEY'RE POWERFUL...

SEÑOR...

?

NOT TO MENTION THAT NOW WE'RE COMPLETELY CUT OFF...

...AND WORN OUT...

ATCHOOO!

WHAT...?!

WHAT DOES IT SAY?

BE AT LAS RAMBLAS THIS AFTERNOON... VISIT THE PARROT-SELLER AND ASK HIM IF HE HAS A TALKATIVE BIRD.

WELL... WHAT DO WE DO?

FIRST, A HOTEL, SO I CAN TAKE OFF THIS DAMN ROBE...

TRUE... DRESSED LIKE THIS WE MUST ALL LOOK LIKE...

LIKE OLD TERRORISTS FROM A FORGOTTEN AGE, PROBABLY...

ATCHOOO!!

THE HOSTAL DE LOS REYES, THEN... IF IT'S STILL THERE... AT LEAST THAT WILL BRING BACK BETTER MEMORIES...

YOU'RE RIGHT, MARIA... WE NEED A PLACE TO REVIVE OURSELVES...

ME, I'VE GOT A COLD FROM ALL THIS STRENUOUS EXERCISE...

THAT'S RIGHT, GOOD IDEA...

HMM... THE PLACE HAS AGED A BIT...

YEAH... LIKE US...

ACTUALLY IT MAKES ME FEEL YOUNGER...

SO WE'LL MEET IN AN HOUR?...

FINE. I CAN'T WAIT TO SEE LAS RAMBLAS AGAIN.

I'M READY!

WELL, LET'S GO PLAY EXOTIC BIRD LOVERS THEN...

SHOULD WE CALL A DOCTOR?

DON'T EVEN THINK ABOUT IT! COLDS CLEAR UP JUST FINE ON THEIR OWN...

YOU'RE NOT SORRY YOU LEFT WARSAW TO COME JOIN US, MARIA?

NOT YET, PRITCH. NOT YET...

30

THERE, LOOK! PARROTS!

THAT MUST BE HIM... LET'S SEE...

AHEM... WE'RE LOOKING FOR A TALKATIVE BIRD...

...CERTAINLY... I HAVE AN EXCELLENT ONE HERE...

WHAT CAN IT SAY?

IT SAYS FOR EXAMPLE THAT YOUR FRIEND ATADELL KEPT BAD COMPANY, AND MADE THE MISTAKE OF TRYING TO GET INFORMATION ON THE BLACK ORDER THROUGH THE HIGHER-UPS IN THE MINISTRY OF THE INTERIOR... PEOPLE WHO PRETENDED THEY HAD FORGOTTEN CERTAIN THINGS STARTED TAKING AN INTEREST IN HIM... THE BLACK ORDER HAS MANY FRIENDS IN THE POLICE FORCE. IN EVERY POLICE FORCE...

AND WHAT ELSE?

IT SAYS THAT WE TOO HAVE OUR INFORMANTS. THE MEN OF THE BLACK ORDER HAVE PULLED OFF TWO SUCCESSFUL ATTACKS IN OUR COUNTRY, BUT THEY HAVE INTERNATIONAL AMBITIONS, AND AREN'T PLANNING TO STAY AROUND HERE VERY LONG, FOR A NUMBER OF REASONS...

THEY'RE SUPPOSED TO LEAVE FOR SICILY LATE TONIGHT. A GREEK SHIP-OWNER SYMPATHETIC TO THEIR PLANS HAS PUT HIS YACHT **NEMESIS** AT THEIR DISPOSAL... THAT'S ALL MY BIRD KNOWS...

TRULY A TALENTED CREATURE...

YES, WELL DONE, POLLY!

I CAN TELL YOU'RE ANXIOUS TO GET BACK TO THE HOTEL AND PLAN OUR STRATEGY, RIGHT PRITCH?

LET'S SAY I'M STARTING TO FEEL HOPEFUL... BUT FIRST...

THIS BOUQUET FOR THE LADY...

MUY BIEN, SEÑOR...

THE DECISION WAS QUICKLY MADE, DESPITE SOME RESERVATOINS. BUT A VOTE WAS REQUIRED...

MY FRIENDS, DO YOU REALLY BELIEVE WE SHOULD STOOP TO THE METHODS OF THESE CRIMINALS?

DON'T BE A PAIN, BARSAC. I'M THE PRIEST HERE, AND I'LL TAKE CARE OF OUR SOULS...

PUT IT TO A VOTE THEN?

GOOD IDEA!

IN THE END, WE ALL RECOGNIZED THAT WE HAD TO AVENGE THE DEAD AND DELIVER A WARNING TO THE BLACK ORDER...

ALRIGHT THEN, CASTEJON WILL TAKE CARE OF FINDING THE NECESSARY EQUIPMENT...

...I HAVE AN EXCELLENT CONTACT FOR THIS SORT OF THING...

WE ALSO HAD TO WATCH THE HARBOR, WHILE MAKING PLANS FOR OUR OWN DEPARTURE...

I'LL KEEP AN EYE ON THE YACHT...

...AND I'LL GO EXPLORE THE DOCKS... IN EXCHANGE FOR SOME PAY-OUTS, I MIGHT MAKE A FEW INTERESTING FRIENDS...

THEY'LL COME IN HANDY, BECAUSE IF WE MAKE THE TYPE OF ATTACK YOU'RE TALKING ABOUT, THERE'LL BE NO WAY WE CAN HANG AROUND HERE FOR LONG...

HEY KATZ, DON'T FORGET DONAHUE'S WAD!

IN CASE WE HAVE TO MAKE A SUDDEN DEPARTURE, I'M GOING TO GET SOME THINGS AT THE PHARMACY FOR DI MANNO... WILL YOU COME WITH ME, MARIA?

NO, KESSLER. I'D RATHER TAKE THE OPPORTUNITY TO SLEEP.. IT'S SHAPING UP TO BE ANOTHER LONG NIGHT...

RIGHT, WE'LL ALL MEET AT THE HARBOR IN THREE HOURS AT THE LATEST...

OK!

ATCHOOO!

ON A WARM NIGHT IN THE GRAND CITY, WE MADE OUR WAY DOWN TO THE HARBOR AS DISCREETLY AS WE COULD...

RENFE METRO

THINK WE'LL DO IT, JUDGE?

IT'LL GO FINE, STRANSKY. DON'T YOU WORRY...

THROUGH THE NARROW STREETS OF THE "BARRIO CHINO", NOTHING WAS EASIER THAN INTERMINGLING WITH THE TIGHTLY PACKED CROWD AS THEY STROLLED PAST ALL THE RESTAURANTS WITH THEIR WARM ODORS...

ALL WAS QUIET ON THE HARBOR...

WELL?

THERE'S THE "NEMESIS". IF YOU ASK ME, THEY'RE NEARLY ALL ABOARD...

...BUT THAT BOAT AT THE DOCK WITH THOSE TWO GREEK SAILORS MEANS THEY'RE STILL WAITING FOR SOMEONE... THAT'S OUR ONLY POSSIBLE TARGET...

EXCELLENT! I HAVE JUST THE THING FOR OUR LATECOMERS...

MY GOD, IT'S AN ANTIQUITY FROM BEFORE THE WAR!

YES... IT'LL BRING BACK MEMORIES FOR THOSE BASTARDS!

ANYWAY, WE'LL HAVE TO ACT QUICKLY...

I'M STILL A GOOD SWIMMER... LET ME DO IT...

LOOK, BARSAC, IF YOU DON'T APPROVE, YOU DON'T HAVE TO DO IT...

IT DOESN'T MATTER, MARIA. AFTER ALL, WE REACHED OUR DECISION DEMOCRATICALLY...

I KNEW YOU HADN'T CHANGED...

IZNALLOZ
BARCELONA

27

34

NOT MUCH WAS LEFT OF THE NIGHT, YET NONETHELESS IT SEEMED A LONG ONE...

IT'S BEEN A LONG TIME SINCE I'VE SEEN MEN DIE, AVIDSEN...

YES, IT'S AN UGLY THING... BUT YOU KNOW, IN MY COUNTRY, AS WELL-POLICED AS IT IS, I'VE SEEN MANY OTHER THINGS, JUST AS UGLY...

THE BITTERSWEET 'HIERBA' ALCOHOL IN THE BACK ROOM OF A FRIENDLY BAR DIDN'T REALLY LIFT OUR SPIRITS...

WE USED DIRTY METHODS, WHICH DIDN'T GIVE US ANY HONOR...

YOU'RE RIGHT, JUDGE... AND THOSE GREEK SAILORS SHOULDN'T HAVE BEEN INVOLVED AT ALL...

YOU'RE NOT GOING TO GIVE US A CRISIS OF FAITH, ARE YOU, BARSAC?

AND THE SAVORY AND SECRET 'TAPAS' OF A BAR WITH UNINQUISITIVE CUSTOMERS DIDN'T REALLY SOOTHE OUR STOMACHS...

COME NOW, YOU KNOW VERY WELL THAT REVOLUTIONARY VIOLENCE ONLY REACTS TO THE VIOLENCE OF THE ESTABLISHED ORDER...

BUT I ALSO KNOW THAT LEFTIST TERRORISM HAS NEVER RESOLVED ANYTHING... IN THE END I'M WONDERING IF I WASN'T WRONG GETTING YOU ALL INVOLVED IN THIS OLD FOLKS' CRUSADE...

IN THE EARLY MORNING, WHEN WE HAD TO MEET **THE AKHIM**, WE WERE ALL SILENT AFTER COLLECTING OUR BAGS... VERY SILENT...

WHICH IN FACT WAS MORE COMFORTABLE... MUCH MORE...

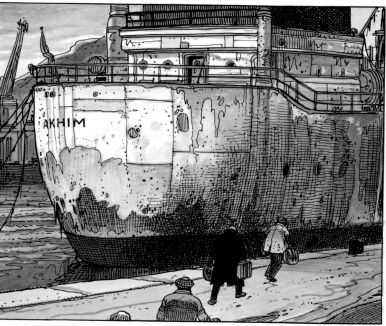

THE CARGO SHIP WAS FILTHY, AND THE COMPARTMENT THAT HAD BEEN SET UP IN THE HOLD REEKED OF VOMIT, URINE, ORANGE PEELS AND CLOVES...

IT WAS IN THOSE CRAMPED QUARTERS THAT WE HAD TO SPEND THE MONOTOUS DAYS OF THE DYING OLD TUB'S LONG VOYAGE...

COUGH COUGH COUGH...

BADLY PLAYED CARD GAMES AND REVOLTING MEALS FOLLOWED ONE AFTER ANOTHER IN THE FOUL COMPARTMENT... *DI MANNO* WAS AS SICK AS A DOG...

· ONE EVENING, DOLPHINS FOLLOWED THE BOAT, PLAYING AROUND IT LIKE WELL-BEHAVED CHILDREN, BRINGING US HOPE AND JOY...

IT WAS ONLY IN SIGHT OF *PALERMO* THAT HE BEGAN TO GET BETTER, WHICH WAS JUST IN TIME...

BECAUSE, AS SOON AS WE WERE SETTLED IN A SQUALID HARBORSIDE HOVEL, WHICH ALLOWED US NOT TO CUT TOO DEEPLY INTO THE CAPITAL BEQUEATHED BY *DONAHUE*, WE HAD TO GET SOME INFORMATION...

...AND THAT WAS UP TO HIM.

I WAS TOLD THAT THE *NEMESIS* PUT INTO PORT HERE SIX DAYS AGO... ABOUT TEN GUYS GOT OFF... AND PFFFT... THAT'S IT...

HMM... TO FIND OUT WHERE THEY WENT, I CAN THINK OF ONLY ONE MAN... *DON CALOGERO VIRZI*...

DON CALOGERO?

YES... AN OLD MAFIOSO...

BUT WILL HE TALK?

I BELIEVE SO... YOU SEE, I STRUGGLED TO HAVE HIM LOCKED UP IN THE FIFTIES. AND HE ATTEMPTED TO HAVE HIS KILLERS KNOCK ME OFF IN THE SIXTIES...

...BOTH OF US FAILED... WHICH IS WHY HE'S FREE, AND I'M ALIVE... NOW HE'S AN OLD DON WHO DOES ME THE HONOR OF CONSIDERING ME ONE OF THE FEW HONEST JUDGES OF HIS LONG CAREER...

AND SINCE I MYSELF HAVE TO ACKNOWLEDGE THAT DESPITE HIS DISHONEST DEALINGS HE AT LEAST HAS DIGNITY, I'LL TRY TO FIND HIM AGAIN...

WE'LL START WITH A SMALL-TIME GANGSTER I KNOW OF... SALVATORE ACCURSIO...

I'LL GO WITH YOU...

WHAT DO YOU MEAN YOU DON'T KNOW DON CALOGERO? TELL ME, SALVATORE, DO YOU HAVE ANY IDEA HOW MANY WARRANTS THERE ARE WITH YOUR NAME ON THEM ON MY DESK IN NAPLES?

UM... ACTUALLY I DO HAVE A LEAD FOR YOU, DOTTORE...

DON CALOGERO? HE HASN'T BEEN IN PALERMO FOR A LONG TIME...

I KNOW, HE RETIRED... BUT WHERE?

SEND THEM TO LEONARDO INSTEAD, SO THEY'LL LEAVE US ALONE!

ONCE INSTALLED IN A HUMBLE PENSION IN THE TRASTEVERE, WE ALL STARTED CHASING CLUES, BECAUSE WE STILL NEEDED TO FIND OUT WHERE THE CONSPIRATORS WERE HANGING OUT... AND SINCE WE COULDN'T WORK IN THE OPEN...

...STRANSKY HOPED THAT GOOD OLD PROLETARIAN INTERNATIONALISM WOULD WORK IN HIS FAVOR WITH HIS OLD COMRADES FROM THE COMMUNIST PARTY...

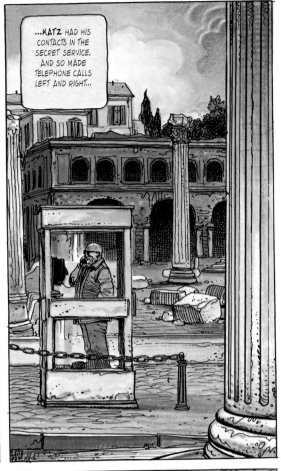

...KATZ HAD HIS CONTACTS IN THE SECRET SERVICE, AND SO MADE TELEPHONE CALLS LEFT AND RIGHT...

AVIDSEN WANTED TO SOUND OUT THE LOCAL SOCIALISTS, OR AT LEAST, WHAT WAS LEFT OF THEM, WHICH COST A LOT IN RESTAURANT BILLS...

DI MANNO MET WITH NASTY-LOOKING POLICE IN FRONT OF BUBBLING FOUNTAINS...

AS FOR MARIA, SHE HAD GOTTEN BACK IN TOUCH WITH FORGOTTEN FRIENDS AND MUCH PREFERRED ATTENDING PARTIES IN AMBER-COLORED PALACES...

AND ONE MORNING, AS THE DAYS WERE GETTING WARMER, SOMEWHERE IN THE RUINS OF THE ROMAN FORUM...

TO THINK THAT THOSE OLD BASTARD COMRADES ARE PRETENDING THEY DON'T KNOW ME ANYMORE SINCE I LEFT PRAGUE, AND THE PARTY!

AS FOR ME, ALL I'VE LEARNED IS THAT ITALIAN COUNTER-INTELLIGENCE ISN'T WORTH A DAMN!

THAT DOESN'T SURPRISE ME... ON THE OTHER HAND THE POLICE KNOW SOMETHING, BUT THE SECRET'S TOO CLOSELY GUARDED FOR MY USUAL INFORMANTS...

AS FOR THE BOURGEOIS POLITICAL PARTIES, THEY'RE TOO INVOLVED WITH STARTING 'COMBINAZIONE' TO WORRY ABOUT THE FUTURE PROBLEMS OF COMMUNISTS, WHICH WOULD BE TO THEIR BENEFIT...

IN SHORT, WE STRUCK OUT EVERYWHERE!

NOT AT ALL, PRITCH... NOT AT ALL!

MARIA! WE GAVE UP WAITING FOR YOU!

WELL, I FOUND OUT THE BLACK ORDER'S HIDING PLACE OVER THE COURSE OF YESTERDAY'S SOIRÉE, BETWEEN THE PISTACHIO SORBET AND THE FRENCH CHAMPAGNE...

HOT DAMN, MARIA!

A YOUNG GUATEMALAN PRELATE HERE FOR AN AUDIENCE WITH THE POPE DROPPED THE INFORMATION WITHOUT REALIZING IT...

...THE YOUNG FOOL WAS DEAD DRUNK AND HAD JUST RETURNED FROM PEEING BEHIND A CLUMP OF CAMELLIAS, WHERE HE HAD OVERHEARD SOMEONE SPEAKING SPANISH...

AH, THE CLERGY THESE DAYS...

FOR GOD'S SAKE, TELL US!!

THEY'RE IN A VERY BEAUTIFUL PALACE IN THE HILLS BEHIND ST. PETER'S...

FRIENDS OF EITHER THE LATE VALERIO BORGHESE, THE BLACK PRINCE, OR THAT CRAZY OLD HAG ELVINA PALLAVICINI!!?

36

EXACTLY, DI MANNO! THE UPPER-CRUST EXTREME-RIGHT ARISTOCRACY WAS THERE IN FULL FORCE!

YOU ALWAYS DID PICK THE MOST REFINED FRIENDS, MARIA...

AHEM... I'M BEGINNING TO UNDERSTAND WHY THE POLICE DIDN'T KNOW ANYTHING... THERE'S SOME HIGH-CLASS PEOPLE INVOLVED...

THAT'S YOUR SPECIALTY, KATZ... SO YOU'LL MAKE THE ARRANGEMENTS...

WITH PLEASURE... BUT WATCH YOUR ARTHRITIS, MY OLD FRIENDS... IF THINGS GO LIKE THEY USUALLY DO...

WHAT DO YOU MEAN?

WE DON'T KNOW HOW THEY'RE GOING TO SET ABOUT IT AND THEY MIGHT STILL HAVE TO DEVISE THEIR PLANS... IT COULD TAKE SOME TIME...

HIGH-CLASS OR NOT, WE'RE FINALLY ABLE TO TAKE ACTION...

EASILY SAID, KESSLER... WE'LL HAVE TO MOUNT A STAKEOUT AND IT COULD TAKE A LONG TIME...

IT TOOK SOME TIME INDEED, AND A GENTLE RAIN WAS FALLING... FLOWERS SPRANG UP AND SO DID OUR ARTHRITIS...

DAMN THAT KATZ! HE WAS RIGHT... I'M ALL SEIZED UP..

HAH. AT OUR AGE, ONLY THE LORD CAN HELP US TO IGNORE OUR EVERYDAY PAINS...

HMM... WHEN YOU'RE THE ONE WHO STARTS TO PRAISE GOD, IT SEEMS MUCH MORE CONVINCING...

IN THE SUBTLEST OF DISGUISES, THAT IS TO SAY THE MOST RIDICULOUS, WE HAD TO STAY IN FRONT OF THE MYSTERIOUS DOORWAY DAY AFTER DAY, THROUGH UNEXPECTED DOWNPOURS...

WHEN THEY WEREN'T ON DUTY, KATZ AND CASTEJON WENT LOOKING TO BUY WEAPONS, AND DIDN'T LET ANYBODY MAKE FUN OF THEM...

CHRIST, KID, IT LOOKS LIKE YOUR STOCK IS AS OLD AND WORN AS OUR ARTERIES!

AH, SO YOU GENTLEMEN ARE CONNOISSEURS... THEN COME THIS WAY...

37

WHILE DI MANNO AND AVIDSEN MET WITH SOME YOUNG TYPES, WHO LAUGHED IN THEIR FACE...

SO WHAT, GRANDAD, WHY DO YOU THINK WE SHOULD CARE IF SOME FAR-RIGHT OLDIES ARE ACTIVE AGAIN?

AFTER THE EXAMPLE OF MORO'S EXECUTION, IT'S A BIT LATE TO GET INTO THE FIELD...

BESIDES, ANYTHING THAT UNDERMINES THE ESTABLISHMENT IS GOOD FOR THE CAUSE... SO WE DON'T CARE ABOUT WHAT MESS YOU'RE IN... FIX IT YOURSELVES...

AS FOR BARSAC AND STRANSKY, THEY ENDEAVORED TO PREPARE THINGS FOR THE NEXT LEG OF THE JOURNEY, WHICH WASN'T GOING TO BE AT ALL FUNNY...

WITH THE LOAD OF SHEEP ON TOP AND YOU UNDERNEATH, WE CAN CROSS ALL OF EUROPE!

SURE, AND DIE OF ASPHYXIA AN HOUR AFTER LEAVING!

...MEANWHILE, MARIA AND KESSLER READ THE NEWS TO PREDICT THE ATTACK, MOSTLY ARTICLES THAT DIDN'T MAKE THEM LAUGH AT ALL...

I BET THEY'LL ACT DURING A PUBLIC DEMONSTRATION...

ME, I'M LEANING TOWARDS AN ABDUCTION BY CAR...

ALL THIS TIME, SPRING WAS APPROACHING. IN THE HILLS OF ROME, THE SCENT OF MIMOSAS WAS ALMOST TOO STRONG...

STRANGE, THESE GOINGS-ON...

YES, THEY'RE GETTING READY FOR SOMETHING...

WHEN THE BLACK ORDER MADE ITS MOVE, IT CAME AS RELIEF BECAUSE ALL OF US HAD BEEN READY FOR THIS DAY WITHOUT KNOWING WHAT IT WOULD ENTAIL...

WHATEVER YOU DO, DON'T LOSE THEM!... I'M GOING TO WARN THE OTHERS!

38

WE'RE ON THE ROAD TO CASSIA...

HEY, THEY'RE TURNING IN...

LOOKS LIKE A CONVENT...

YES, THE PERPETUAL ADORATION OF THE HOLY SHROUD! BUT I ALSO HEARD AN OLD COUNTESS TALKING ABOUT A VERY PRIVATE CLINIC AT THE BACK OF THE GARDEN WHERE THE EXTREMELY WEALTHY GO TO MEND THEMSELVES...

WELL, WELL... I BELIEVE I HAVE A PROPOSAL TO MAKE TONIGHT, THEN...

INDEED, THAT NIGHT, AFTER AN EXHAUSTING DAY OF LAYING LOW, IT WAS THE TIME FOR PROPOSALS...

WHEW... TODAY WAS HARD... IS EVERYONE HERE?

YES, BY SOME MIRACLE! THANKS TO OUR LUCK, THE POLICE AREN'T TALKING ABOUT ANYONE ELSE BUT US!

KESSLER, AT LAST!!!

THAT'S IT! THE BLACK ORDER BRIGADE JUST CLAIMED RESPONSIBILITY FOR THE ATTACK AND ARE DEMANDING A BILLION-LIRA RANSOM!

IF THE COMMUNIST PARTY'S AS LOW ON FUNDS AS THEY CLAIM, COMRADE TRAVIANI IS IN TROUBLE...

IN ANY CASE IT'S TIME TO START THINKING ABOUT LEAVING THE COUNTRY QUICKLY... WE WON'T EVADE THE NET THEY'RE PUTTING IN PLACE FOR MUCH LONGER...

I'VE FOUND AN OLD ARMY PILOT WHO'S PREPARED TO FLY US OUT DISCREETLY IN EXCHANGE FOR THE LAST SCRAPINGS OF DONAHUE'S LEGACY...

YES, BUT WHERE TO?

QUITE SO... NOW, WE'RE THE ONLY ONES WHO KNOW WHERE THAT BASTARD VALIÑO IS. IF HE'S STILL ALIVE WE HAVE TO MAKE HIM TALK SO WE CAN FIND OUT WHERE THE BLACK ORDER TOOK THE DEPUTY...

AS COWARDLY AS HE IS CRUEL, GENERAL VALIÑO... THAT'S WHAT THEY SAID DURING THE GUERRA CIVIL...

WHAT A GOOD IDEA... TORTURING THE TORTURER...

43

49

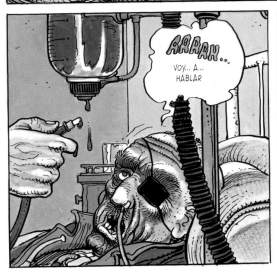

AND AS DAYLIGHT CRESTED THE HILLS, NEAR A TINY AIRFIELD WELL-HIDDEN BY CYPRESS TREES...

HERE COME OUR THREE TORTURERS...

YES...

AND?

WE'RE OFF TO SWITZERLAND...

WHAT DID HE SAY EXACTLY?

NOT VERY MUCH... HE PASSED OUT FROM FRIGHT AND NEVER HAD TIME TO TELL US WHERE THE BLACK ORDER IS EXACTLY...

...THE ONLY THING FOR CERTAIN IS THAT DESPITE VARIOUS ANONYMOUS DONATIONS, THEY NEED MONEY TOO. THE RANSOM WILL BE PAID THROUGH GENEVA, WHERE THE ORDER HAS STRONG BANKING CONNECTIONS...

THAT WAY THEY CAN KILL TWO BIRDS WITH ONE STONE... DISCREDIT THE COMMUNISTS AND REFILL THEIR COFFERS...

...IF THEY PAY...

BAH...

LET'S HURRY. WE HAVE TO LEAVE BEFORE SUNRISE...

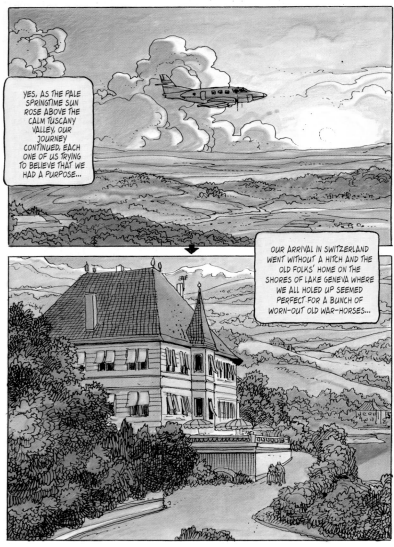

YES, AS THE PALE SPRINGTIME SUN ROSE ABOVE THE CALM TUSCANY VALLEY, OUR JOURNEY CONTINUED, EACH ONE OF US TRYING TO BELIEVE THAT WE HAD A PURPOSE...

OUR ARRIVAL IN SWITZERLAND WENT WITHOUT A HITCH AND THE OLD FOLKS' HOME ON THE SHORES OF LAKE GENEVA WHERE WE ALL HOLED UP SEEMED PERFECT FOR A BUNCH OF WORN-OUT OLD WAR-HORSES...

IN FACT, THINKING BACK, OUR ARRIVAL IS THE ONLY THING THAT WENT WELL... PERHAPS BECAUSE WE REALLY NO LONGER HAD A PURPOSE...

PERHAPS BECAUSE OUR WILL WAS ERODED BY THE SIGHT OF THE DECREPITUDE OF THE OTHER OLD DOTARDS SPENDING THE DAY STARING OUT UPON A LAKE AS CLOUDED AS THEIR EYES?

146

EVEN THE CLUMSY ANTICS OF SCIENTIFIC SOCIALISM DIDN'T MAKE ANY OF US LAUGH...

THE GENERAL SECRETARIES OF THE EUROPEAN COMMUNIST PARTIES GATHERED TODAY IN PARIS. AFTER REJECTING, ACCORDING TO RELIABLE SOURCES, AN OFFER OF FINANCIAL ASSISTANCE FROM **COMECON**, THEY ARE CONTEMPLATING TAKING UP AN INTERNATIONAL COLLECTION TO PAY THE RANSOM FOR DEPUTY TRAVIANI, NOW KIDNAPPED THREE DAYS AGO... BUT OTHER MORE DISCREET MEANS MAY...

THINK THEY'LL COUGH UP MARIA?

I DON'T CARE...

WHILE WAITING FOR THINGS TO GET STARTED AGAIN, THE FORCED INACTIVITY MADE OUR BRAINS START WORKING ALMOST IN SPITE OF THEMSELVES...

LOOK, ANOTHER ARTICLE ON THE BLACK ORDER BRIGADE... NOT VERY WELL-INFORMED BUT IT'S STILL GOOD NEWS IF IT GETS THE POLICE AFTER THEM...

YEAH... EXCEPT I'VE JUST READ ONE ON US. JUST AS POORLY-INFORMED, BUT IT'S STILL BAD NEWS... AND FOR THE SAME REASONS, IF YOU TAKE MY MEANING...

HMM... IN DENMARK THEY'RE STILL CONCERNED ABOUT THE DISAPPEARANCE OF THE MINISTER AVIDSEN...

LUCKY DEVIL...

YEAH RIGHT...

WHEREAS MY NEWSPAPER DOESN'T EVEN SEEM TO NOTICE I'M GONE... TOO BAD...

AND I HAVE THE STRANGE IMPRESSION THAT PHILOSOPHICAL THOUGHT IN GERMANY CONTINUES TO ADVANCE WITHOUT ME...

YEAH... WE ALL MEAN VERY LITTLE, BUT ESPECIALLY IN THE SPY GAME, WHERE ONE DISAPPEARED MAN MORE OR LESS...

AT OUR AGE WE HAVE TO START GETTING USED TO THE IDEA OF RETURNING TO OBLIVION...

REALLY! YOU KNOW YOU'RE ALL SERIOUSLY STARTING TO GET ON MY NERVES, YOU BUNCH OF HAS-BEENS!?!

AS FOR ME, I'M A WOMAN, AND I STILL HAVE A TASTE FOR LIFE...

...SO IF YOU GUYS WANT TO SIT HERE RETURNING TO OBLIVION WHILE DREAMING ABOUT MAKING MINOR CHANGES TO HISTORY IN THE MIDDLE OF AN OLD FOLKS' HOME, GO RIGHT AHEAD! BUT NOT ME! SEE YOU LATER!!!

BUT, MARIA!?

HOLY GOD!

WHAT A WOMAN!

WHAT CLASS!

WELL, SINCE THAT'S HOW IT IS, I'M OFF TO FIND A DISCREET BORDELLO IN GENEVA... AFTER YEARS OF IMPOSED ABSTINENCE, I'M SURE THE LORD WILL BE UNDERSTANDING...

...PERHAPS IF I COULD FIND A COMFORTABLE BAR, WITH LEATHER SOFAS AND RARE LIQUOR...

MARIA HAS A POINT... WE'RE WASTING GOOD TIMES... I'M GOING TO GO RENT A BOAT... I ALWAYS HOPED THAT I WOULD CATCH AT LEAST ONE FISH BEFORE I DIED...

INDEED!

PUFF PUFF

WE HAVE FINE TASTES...

OUR DEAR COMRADES MAKE ME LAUGH WITH THEIR TASTE FOR LUXURY... RECREATIONAL BOATING, CALL-GIRLS, AND FINE LIQUEURS, I ASK YOU! WE DON'T HAVE A CENT LEFT...

AND IF I TRIED TO MAKE CONTACT WITH THE NETWORK OF EXILES FROM ALL PARTS THAT I KNOW IN SWITZERLAND?

NOW THAT'S AN IDEA... WHEN ALL'S SAID AND DONE, I ALSO HAVE A NUMBER OF CONTACTS IN THE REVOLVING HUB OF NETWORKS IN THIS SCENIC DEMOCRATIC COUNTRY...

MMM... SINCE AT THE MOMENT NOBODY KNOWS WHERE WE ARE, GO AHEAD IF YOU CAN DO IT WITH CAUTION... BUT THAT DOESN'T RESOLVE OUR FINANCIAL PROBLEMS AT ALL....

JUST A MINUTE! IF YOU ALLOW ME TO DIP INTO THE FUNDS TO BUY A NICE SUIT AND GO TO A GOOD HAIRDRESSER, I MIGHT HAVE A CUSHY JOB...

WHAT KIND?

OH, JUST A HARMLESS LITTLE ANNOUNCEMENT IN THE "FINANCIAL TIMES"...

...BUT FOR THOSE WHO CAN READ BETWEEN THE LINES I BELIEVE THEY'RE LOOKING FOR A TRAVELLING BANKER...

AND WHAT'S THAT?

YES, TELL US ABOUT IT...

OH, MY COMRADES, I SEE THAT IT'S POSSIBLE FOR THE OLD ANTI-IMPERIALIST VANGUARD, BOLDLY BATTLING THE GREAT MASS OF INTERNATIONAL CAPITAL, TO BE UNAWARE OF A FEW THINGS....

ALRIGHT, SO WE HAVEN'T ALL BEEN INVOLVED IN UPPER-LEVEL BOURGEOIS POLITICS...

WELL NOW, WOULD YOU BELIEVE IT'S JUST A SMALL JOB, CONSISTING FOR EXAMPLE OF GAMBLING ON CURRENCY DEVALUATIONS AND MOVEMENTS OF THE STOCK MARKET... AND, UM... OF CARRYING MONEY INTO OTHER COUNTRIES... TO KEEP THINGS BALANCED, AS THEY SAY...

WORK INVOLVING UTMOST DISCRETION, IT MUST BE SAID, WITH VERY, VERY LARGE COMMISSIONS...

I SEE...

MMHM...

SO WHAT DO YOU SAY?

I'LL TAKE YOU TO AN ENGLISH TAILOR I USED TO KNOW...

AS FOR ME, I WAS A BARBER AT MY CONCENTRATION CAMP, BUT I THINK YOU NEED SOMETHING A LITTLE MORE RESPECTABLE...

THE WEATHER BECAME FINE AND FRESH OVER THE LAKE. OCCASIONALLY BIRDS WOULD SKIM THE SILVERY SURFACE OF THE WATER...

DI MANNO STILL HADN'T CAUGHT ANYTHING, AND SPENT WHOLE DAYS IN HIS BOAT, STARING AT HIS MOTIONLESS LURE...

CASTEJON WAS SULLEN AND GRUMBLED THAT HE WAS PAST THE AGE OF HAVING TO ASK FOR POCKET MONEY TO GO INTO TOWN...

BARSAC TOOK LONG WALKS IN THE COUNTRY AND TOLD TALES ABOUT TREES IN BLOOM, WHICH NOBODY LISTENED TO...

MARIA HAD DISAPPEARED BUT A PICTURE OF HER CHATTING IN THE MIDDLE OF A GROUP OF YOUNG ARTISTS WAS PUBLISHED IN THE PAPER, AND IT LOOKED LIKE SHE WAS HAVING FUN...

KESSLER READ THICK BOOKS THROUGHOUT THE DAY AND TALKED ABOUT RECOMMENCING WORK ON HIS EPISTEMIOLOGY THESIS, BUT NOBODY LISTENED TO HIM EITHER...

THE NEWS ALMOST NEVER MENTIONED THE DEPUTY TRAVIANI ANY MORE, WHICH MEANT THAT THE NEGOTIATIONS WERE GOING WELL...

IN ITALY, IT'S THE TWENTY-THIRD ROUND OF THE ELECTIONS...

OLD VALIÑO DIED WITHOUT A FUSS AND ONLY MADRID'S "ABC" ANNOUNCED THE NEWS, ON PAGE THIRTEEN...

AVIDSEN, CARRYING PRETTY FAWN-COLORED LEATHER BRIEFCASES, MADE REPEATED TRIPS BETWEEN FRANCE AND SWITZERLAND WITH A SCHEDULE SO FRENZIED THAT IT HARDLY LEFT HIM THE TIME TO BRING US A FEW TIDY SUMS OF MONEY...

REMEMBER TO GET THE PHOTOS I ASKED FOR...

DON'T WORRY!

BUT FINALLY ONE EVENING, KATZ AND STRANSKY RETURNED IN A HAPPY MOOD...

I'VE GOT A LEAD...

ME TOO...

AHA, THINGS ARE MOVING AGAIN...

I BELIEVE I KNOW WHERE THEIR HIDEOUT IS...

SOME VERBENA?

AND I BELIEVE I'VE UNCOVERED HOW THE RANSOM IS TO BE PAID...

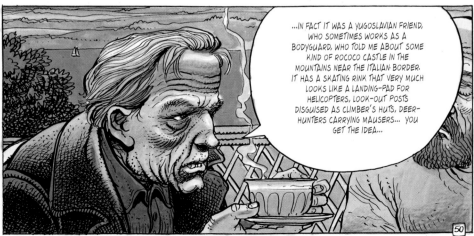

...IN FACT IT WAS A YUGOSLAVIAN FRIEND, WHO SOMETIMES WORKS AS A BODYGUARD, WHO TOLD ME ABOUT SOME KIND OF ROCOCO CASTLE IN THE MOUNTAINS NEAR THE ITALIAN BORDER. IT HAS A SKATING RINK THAT VERY MUCH LOOKS LIKE A LANDING-PAD FOR HELICOPTERS, LOOK-OUT POSTS DISGUISED AS CLIMBER'S HUTS, DEER-HUNTERS CARRYING MAUSERS... YOU GET THE IDEA...

50

I HAVE A... UM... RELIABLE CORRESPONDENT WHO WORKS IN THE BANK. WELL, WOULD YOU BELIEVE THAT A ORDINARILY VERY STABLE FIRM, INTERNATIONALLY KNOWN FOR ITS SECRET NUMBERED ACCOUNTS, IS UNDERGOING A FLURRY OF ACTIVITY? IT'S CALLED THE CREDIT MEDITERRANEAN...

ALL VERY INTERESTING... AT LAST WE CAN TAKE ACTION!

TAKE ACTION -- WHAT ELSE COULD WE DO NOW? BESIDES WOULDN'T IT BE BETTER THAN JUST THINKING? THE DAY AFTERWARDS, WE WERE AT BATTLE-STATIONS...

I'LL BE STAYING HERE... I STILL HAVEN'T CAUGHT ANYTHING...

AS YOU PREFER, MY FRIEND...

BUT THE CASTLE LOOKED A LOT LIKE A FORTRESS...

HUFF...

I CAN'T GO ON...

HAND ME THE BINOCULARS, PRITCH...

WHAT A PLACE!

TO THINK THOSE BASTARDS JUST TRAVEL BY HELICOPTER...

SO DID THE BANK, AS WELL...

WHAT COULD BE GOING ON BEHIND THOSE WALLS?

MY FRIEND, ONLY GOD AND THE INTERNATIONAL COMMUNIST PARTY KNOW FOR SURE...

WE HAD TO MAKE A PLAN. OR SO WE ALL THOUGHT...

WE'D NEED CANNONS TO TAKE THAT CASTLE!

AND MORTARS TO GET INTO THAT BANK!

YEAH...

A HIDING PLACE SUSPECTED TO HAVE BEEN USED BY THE KIDNAPPERS WAS DESERTED...

DESERTED?!!

WHAT DO YOU KNOW...

ŞARAP?

ÇOK, THANK YOU.

IT IS NOT KNOWN WHERE, WHEN, OR EVEN WHETHER THE RANSOM WAS PAID. AT PRESENT, THE ITALIAN COMMUNIST PARTY IS REFUSING TO COMMENT. SWISS BANKING AGENCIES DON'T KNOW ANYTHING ABOUT IT...

VERY ELEGANTLY DONE!!!

THE MAN WHO DIED ON LAKE GENEVA HAS BEEN IDENTIFIED. GIANCARLO DI MANNO, THE MINOR ITALIAN JUDGE WHO WAS BURIED THIS AFTERNOON, WAS ALSO A FORMER MEMBER OF THE INTERNATIONAL BRIGADES, AND HIS TIES TO THE EXTREME LEFT HAVE NOW BEEN CONFIRMED...

POOR OLD MAN! BURIED ALONE IN THE DIRT, LIKE A DOG... WHAT A PITY...

I PRAY FOR HIM...

BAH

MEANWHILE, INVESTIGATIONS CONTINUE WITH HOPES OF FINDING A GROUP THAT COULD BE SIGNING THEIR ATTACKS IN THE NAME OF THE BLACK ORDER, IN ORDER TO THROW SUSPICION ONTO THE EXTREME RIGHT...

HA HA... SEE THERE, HOW TALENTED THE SWISS POLICE CAN BE...

TALENTED AT THROWING UP A SMOKE-SCREEN, SURE...

WE'RE UP TO OUR NECKS IN HOT WATER NOW...

TOO TRUE...

AND MY TURKISH FRIENDS DON'T WANT US TO TAKE ANY ACTION AT ALL... TOO RISKY FOR THEM...

WHAT DO YOU MEAN, YOU'VE BEEN EXPECTING OUR CALL?

YES, YES... DON'T MOVE. I'M COMING WITH MARIA AND WE'LL PICK YOU UP.

WE HAVE TO CONTACT AVIDSEN!...

MMM... HE LEFT ME A NUMBER... A SECURE ONE, APPARENTLY...

LET'S TRY IT... HE'S THE ONLY ONE WHO CAN GET US OUT OF HERE...

WHAT HAPPENED AFTER THAT IS INDEED A BLUR... EVERYTHING STARTED MOVING TOO FAST...

BUT MARIA, WHAT ARE YOU DOING HERE?

I'D LIKE YOU ALL TO MEET MY NEW BOYFRIEND, VICTOR. HE'S A FILM-MAKER...

AND AVIDSEN, HOW DID YOU DO IT?

I'LL EXPLAIN LATER... THE BORDERS ARE SEALED, BUT VICTOR HAS AN AUTHORIZATION FROM SWISS TELEVISION TO SHOOT IN GERMANY... YOU GUYS WILL BE THE TECHNICAL CREW...

...AS FAR AS THE BORDER, ANYWAY, BECAUSE THE REAL CREW WENT BY PLANE YESTERDAY...

I SEE...

WE SHOULD GET GOING...

HERE ARE FAKE DOCUMENTS WITH YOUR PHOTOS, MY FRIENDS. DONE BY AN EXPERT, AS YOU CAN SEE...

YOU DIDN'T WASTE ANY TIME...

AH, BEING A TRAVELLING BANKER IS LIKE BEING A MINISTER. IT'S A GOOD JOB IF YOU DON'T DO IT FOR TOO LONG. INSTEAD OF DELIVERING MY LAST SUITCASE, I STARTED PUTTING IT TO GOOD USE, AS YOU CAN SEE...

AND MARIA?

WHEN I CALLED HER, SHE HAD ALREADY WORKED EVERYTHING OUT AND MADE PREPARATIONS...

QUIET BACK THERE!

CALM DOWN, VICTOR DEAR... THESE POLICE LOOK REASSURINGLY STUPID TO ME...

55

BITTE...

LISTEN, I'M NOT WITHOUT CONTACTS IN THE UNIVERSITIES AND OTHER PLACES...

IF YOU GIVE ME SOME TIME, I'M SURE I CAN UNCOVER THE BLACK ORDER'S TRAIL... WHAT DO YOU SAY?

AND YOUR THESIS ON EPISTEMIOLOGY?

TOO BAD FOR EPISTEMIOLOGY. I'LL ALWAYS HAVE TIME TO WRITE IT LATER...

DO YOU HAVE ANY MONEY LEFT, AVIDSEN?

PLENTY. AND IT HAPPENS TO BE IN DEUTSCHMARKS...

...BUT NOT MUCH TIME WAS LEFT FOR HANS KESSLER, EMINENT PHILOSOPHER AND PROFESSOR AT HEIDELBERG UNIVERSITY...

WONDERFUL. WE CAN RENT A CAR!

BUT HE DIDN'T KNOW THAT AS HE SET OFF ON HIS PECULIAR QUEST...

WHERE TO?

FIRST, BAVARIA...

HOWEVER, AFTER A SERIES OF MEETINGS, IT ALL BECAME MURKY, AND THE BLACK ORDER SUDDENLY SEEMED UNREAL THROUGH THE SMOKE OF THE BEER-CELLARS...

NOBODY HAD HEARD ANYTHING. NOBODY EVEN SEEMED INTERESTED...

SUMMER HAD ARRIVED, AND, IN THE THICK HEAT OF THE CITY, A TYPE OF NUMBNESS SEEMED TO PENETRATE OUR WEARY BODIES...

WHAT IMPRESSION DID THE FORGOTTEN SURVIVORS OF FORGOTTEN BRIGADES MAKE ON THE YOUNG CROWD, WITH THEIR LIVELY WITS AND STEADY HANDS? NOT MUCH OF ONE, CERTAINLY...

AND AS FRANKFURT FOLLOWED MUNICH, WHAT IMPRESSION WAS MADE ON THE OLD MEN WITH DROOPING FLESH BY THE YOUNG GIRLS WITH SUPPLE BODIES WHO SPOKE OF GENTLE TACTICS AND NON-REPRESSIVE SCHOOLS? NOT MUCH OF ONE EITHER, PROBABLY...

TWO LINES OF ACTION, TWO BASTIONS OF HOPE, AND MANY CRUEL PIECES OF HISTORY, ALL INTERSECTING WHERE NEITHER SIDE HAD MUCH TO SAY TO THE OTHER...

LOTTE, I'M SO HAPPY TO SEE YOU!

ME TOO, PROFESSOR!

BUT IT COULDN'T BE DENIED THAT KESSLER, THROUGH EPISTEMIOLOGY OR THROUGH OTHER THINGS, HAD A WHOLE LOT OF CONTACTS, AND, ONE FINE DAY, SOMEWHERE ON THE BANKS OF THE RHINE, IT ALL CAME TOGETHER...

IT WAS ONE OF HIS FORMER STUDENTS, NOW A FREE-LANCE JOURNALIST FOR THE EXTREME LEFT, WHO PUT US BACK ON COURSE...

BUT I'M TELLING YOU IT'S TRUE... A GUY I INTERVIEWED ALMOST BY CHANCE TOLD ME ABOUT IT IN ORDER TO SHOW OFF.. I DIDN'T PAY MUCH ATTENTION AT THE TIME...

...AND NOW JUST TWO DAYS AGO, WHEN I BECAME SURE HE **REALLY** WAS A MEMBER OF THE **VIKING JUGEND**...

AND WHAT'S THAT?...

A SMALL AND LITTLE-KNOWN BUT ACTIVE NEO-NAZI GROUP..

IT WAS THE VIKING JUGEND THAT HID YOUR OLD MEN WHEN THEY CROSSED OVER INTO GERMANY, I'M SURE OF IT... THEY ARRIVED BY HELICOPTER IN THE SUBURBS AROUND HAMBURG...

HMM... THAT COULD FIT...

AND NOW THEY'RE PLANNING SOMETHING BIG IN HOLLAND WITH YOUNG GUYS LIKE THE BASTARD THAT I EVEN HAD TO SLEEP WITH JUST TO GET SOME INFORMATION OUT OF HIM...

WELL, HAPPY TO BE BACK IN ACTION, CASTEJON?

OH YES, DEFINITELY!!!

AND YOU, STRANSKY?

RFF...

58

ME, I'M NOT UPSET TO BE LEAVING THIS COUNTRY... TOO MANY UNPLEASANT FAMILY MEMORIES...

I WANT TO LEAVE TOO... AND SINCE I FINALLY HAVE A SCOOP I MIGHT AS WELL MAKE THE MOST OUT OF IT BY STAYING WITH YOU GUYS...

AND YOUR YOUNG VIKING?

I DUMPED THE BASTARD YESTERDAY, THANK GOD...

KESSLER WAS HAPPY AND WE WEREN'T TOO SURE WHETHER IT WAS BECAUSE HE HAD DELIVERED AS PROMISED OR BECAUSE LOTTE'S SMILE WARMED HIS OLD BONES...

BUT HE DIDN'T STAY HAPPY FOR LONG, BECAUSE, JUST AS WE NEARED THE DUTCH BORDER...

SHALL WE TAKE A WALK AND STRETCH OUR LEGS?

SURE, PROFESSOR!

IT MIGHT BE A FLASHY TRUCK BUT IT SURE IS UNCOMFORTABLE...

SAY, WHAT DO YOU SUPPOSE...?!!!

EVERYBODY DOWN!!!

59

65

66

IN HOLLAND, THINGS ONCE AGAIN BEGAN DEVELOPING TOO FAST FOR OUR TIRED MINDS, ALREADY WORN BY THE PACES WE'D PUT THEM THROUGH. IT TOOK US ONLY ONE NIGHT IN AMSTERDAM TO DISCOVER THAT KESSLER HAD DIED FOR NOTHING...

WE SHOULD GET SOMETHING TO EAT, ANYWAY...

YOU THINK SO?

BECAUSE THE ORDER WAS WELL AND TRULY THERE, EVEN IF WE DIDN'T KNOW WHERE EXACTLY...

DAAR KOMEN DE SAUCIJSJES!

STRANGE CROWD GATHERING OUTSIDE...

LET'S GO FIND OUT...

WHAT'S HAPPENING?

AN ATTACK...

SOME EXPLOSIONS! THEY'RE SAYING DOZENS ARE DEAD...

THE POLICE AREN'T EVEN THERE YET...

LUCKILY THE RADIO WAS THERE TO COVER THE FESTIVAL, OTHERWISE...

...DE VERWARRING IS ALGEHEEL...

BUT WHAT ARE THEY SAYING?!

...HANG ON!... THEY'VE JUST RECEIVED A STATEMENT...

...SIGNED BY THE BLACK ORDER BRIGADE...

SAINTS ALIVE...

BUT WE LOOK LIKE FOOLS! FOOLS FOR ARRIVING TOO LATE AGAIN!!!

YOU SHOULD BE ASHAMED TO WORRY ABOUT WHAT WE LOOK LIKE DURING SUCH A TRAGEDY, CASTEJON...

61

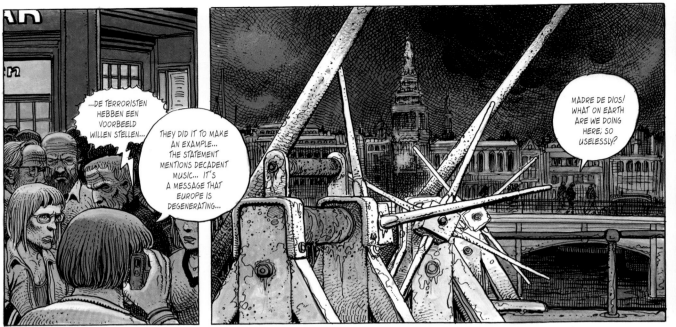

BOATS MOVING TO AND FRO IN THE DARK AND MISTY SUMMER NIGHT...

MUTILATED CORPSES AND THE WAILING WOUNDED BEING CARRIED THROUGH THE CONFUSION...

SPOTLIGHTS SLICING THROUGH TREES WITH RUSTLING LEAVES...

AND ABOVE ALL, AN IMPRESSION OF CONSTANT, CONSTANT VIOLENCE...

MAKE WAY! MAKE WAY!!

LET ME THROUGH, FOR PITY'S SAKE!!!

YOU BASTARDS, HIS KID IS DYING!

MIND YOUR OWN BUSINESS, ASSHOLE!

LOOKS LIKE TWO GUYS FROM THE BLACK ORDER WERE KILLED ON THE SPOT!

ONE OF THE DEVICES WAS BADLY PLACED...

WHERE?

THERE...

YES, BITTER ABSURDITY...

AND PERHAPS EVEN AN IMPRESSION OF ABSURDITY...

I DON'T GET IT, MAN, DID WE TAKE TOO BIG A DOSE...?

ME, I JUST HAD A LITTLE JOINT...

NO MORE MUSIC?

GO TO SLEEP JOOP, IT'S JUST A BAD TRIP..

WHERE'RE WE HEADED?

DON'T KNOW...

HEY, I FOUND SOME RIVER MAPS...

THAT'S A START...

AND I JUST HEARD SOMETHING ON THE RADIO...

WELL?

...IT SEEMS THE BRIGADE HAS LEFT ITS LAIR, A SMALL CARGO BOAT ALONG THE NOORDOOST POLDER... THEY MENTIONED A HELICOPTER HEADING TOWARDS THE SOUTH...

SO WE GO SOUTH!

WELL, IT'S NOT AS IF WE CAN TAKE THE BOAT TO THE NORTH SEA, ANYWAY...

AHEM... THERE'S ONE MORE THING... KESSLER AND THE GIRL HAVE BEEN FOUND...

...AND INTERPOL HAS ISSUED A WARRANT FOR OUR ARREST...

WELL AT LEAST THEY'VE STOPPED CONFUSING US WITH THOSE OTHER BASTARDS...

SOME COMFORT...

NOT TO MENTION THAT IT WON'T MAKE OUR TRIP ANY EASIER...

NOT THE WAY THINGS ARE...

66

IN FACT, THE SLOW JOURNEY SOUTH WENT WITHOUT A HITCH. IT SEEMED THAT AVIDSEN'S STASH WAS INEXHAUSTIBLE...

WILLMA

IT ALLOWED US TO RE-PAINT THE BARGE AND A LOT OF OTHER THINGS BESIDES. PERHAPS WE WERE EVEN STARTING TO BECOME GOOD SAILORS...

BUT NOBODY TALKED TO EACH OTHER ANYMORE. AND THE DAYS DRAGGED ON LIKE THOUGHTS, OR MEMORIES...

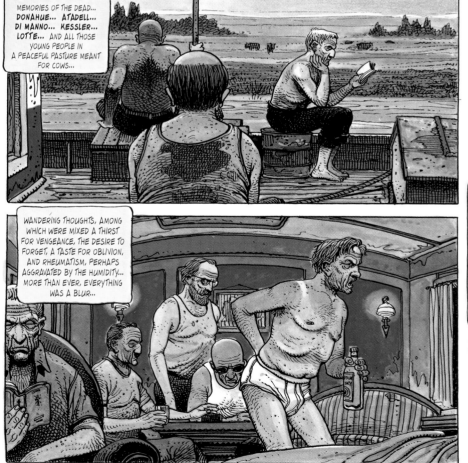

MEMORIES OF THE DEAD... DONAHUE... ATADELL... DI MANNO... KESSLER... LOTTE... AND ALL THOSE YOUNG PEOPLE IN A PEACEFUL PASTURE MEANT FOR COWS...

WANDERING THOUGHTS, AMONG WHICH WERE MIXED A THIRST FOR VENGEANCE, THE DESIRE TO FORGET, A TASTE FOR OBLIVION, AND RHEUMATISM, PERHAPS AGGRAVATED BY THE HUMIDITY... MORE THAN EVER, EVERYTHING WAS A BLUR...

I'LL GO TELEPHONE, JUST IN CASE...

OUR ARRIVAL IN PARIS WAS MADE QUIETLY. AUTUMN HAD BEGUN TO COLOR THE TREES ON THE ÎLE DE LA GRANDE JATTE. LEAVES WERE CLINGING TO MOORINGS ON THE JETTY...

61

74

TWO WEEKS LATER, IT WAS TIME FOR SOME BICYCLE TOURING. BUT NOW THE WARM DAYS WERE FAR BEHIND US, AND THE WIND BLEW VIOLENTLY ACROSS THE MILLEVACHES PLATEAU...

MY... HUFF.. ACHING KNEES...

CAN YOU... HUFF... SEE THE TOP?

WE'RE NEVER GOING TO GET THERE...

JUST KEEP GOING!

WITH ALL THE EQUIPMENT LOADED INTO BAGS ON THE BICYCLES, THE DRIZZLE-SWEPT MOUNTAIN WAS A TOUGH RIDE, EVEN ON THE WAY DOWN...

WE DEFINITELY COULD HAVE MADE OTHER ARRANGEMENTS...

THIS ISN'T THE TIME TO DISCUSS IT!

YOU ALL KNOW VERY WELL THERE'S NO OTHER WAY TO APPROACH THEIR HIDEOUT WITHOUT AROUSING SUSPICION...

THERE IT IS! AN OLD FARMHOUSE REFITTED WITH MODERN COMFORTS... THEY HAVE EVERYTHING THEY NEED... FIRING RANGES... ALL KINDS OF WEAPONS... AND GUARDS PATROLLING DAY AND NIGHT...

IT'S TIME TO GO DOWN...

LISTEN, BARSAC... I WANTED TO TELL YOU...

EAH?

WE UNDERSTAND YOUR CONVICTIONS...

BAH, THERE'S NOTHING WORSE THAN LAYMEN MORALIZING. HIJO DE PUTA, LET'S GO!

TO THE PRESENT!!!

HERE, PASS ME THE FOIE GRAS...

HEADS UP!

THIS IS IT, HERE THEY COME...

WHAT ARE YOU DOING HERE?

JUST WHAT IT LOOKS LIKE... HAVING A PICNIC!

...DIDN'T YOU KNOW THIS IS PRIVATE PROPERTY?

UM, NO...

YOU'RE GOING TO HAVE TO CLEAR OFF IMMEDIATELY!

HEY, LISTEN... IT'S JUST A VETERAN'S RALLY...

WE ALL USED TO BE COMPETITORS IN THE TOUR DE FRANCE...

OH YEAH? THAT'S INTERESTING, BECAUSE MY BROTHER-IN-LAW USED TO...

WELL, DON'T STAND HERE CHATTING WITH THESE OLD FOOLS, JOE!

71

HOW TO RECOUNT THE THINGS THAT NEXT CAME TO PASS IN THAT PLACE ALREADY ENCRUSTED WITH THE COLD OF THE COMING WINTER?

THE DRUNKEN GUARD WAS NEUTRALIZED AS PLANNED, AND HIS TWO DOGS BARELY HAD TIME TO BARK...

WE HAD ALSO ANTICIPATED THE FIRST SOUNDING OF THE ALARM, WHICH REMAINED WITHOUT CONSEQUENCE...

WHAZZAT?

AH, MUST BE JUST JOSEPH BEATING HIS HOUNDS!

BY THE WAY, I JUST SAW THOSE OLD GUYS GET ON THEIR WAY AGAIN...

A FEW MINUTES LATER, THE MACHINE GUN WAS LINED UP WITH THE MAIN DOOR...

PASS ME THAT CLIP!

THE ONLY THING LEFT WAS TO QUIETLY SET THE PLASTIC EXPLOSIVE CHARGES. EVERYTHING SEEMED TO PROGRESS AS SMOOTHLY AND AS INEVITABLY AS A NIGHTMARE, WITH ITS HORRIBLE LOGIC...

IT WAS A STRANGE FEELING, FINALLY SEEING THE MEN WE HAD FOLLOWED FOR SO LONG, SO CLOSE TO US...

JOAQUIN DE VALLELLANO, THE GUERILLA FROM CHRIST THE KING, HAVING A FOOTBATH...

DU BUSQUET, A SURVIVOR OF VICHY AND THE OAS, HALF-HEARTEDLY PAWING THE LOCAL HELP...

JAVIER, ASSASSIN FROM THE LEGION AZUL, QUIETLY READING THE LIVES OF THE SAINTS...

COLPIN, THE FRENCH MERCENARY, PLAYING DARTS WITH HIS ITALIAN FRIEND WITH A ROOMFUL OF MEN DRINKING BEER...

CONTEMPTIBLE OLD MEN, BEING WATCHED BY OTHER OLD MEN, PERHAPS JUST AS CONTEMPTIBLE...

WITHOUT A DOUBT, HELL IS WHAT THEY DESERVED, AND WITHOUT A DOUBT WE DESERVED IT AS MUCH AS THEY DID...

BECAUSE HELL IS WHAT IT WAS!

LET'S GO BROTHERS!!!

74

HELL FOR JOAQUIN DE VALLELLANO...

HA HA HA!

FOR FELIPE CASTEJON...

...FOR PAVEL STRANSKY AND EPHRAIM KATZ...

FOR CHARLES DU BUSQUET AND EVEN FOR PAUL-MARIE BARSAC, THE SOLDIER WHO THOUGHT HE COULD RENOUNCE VIOLENCE...

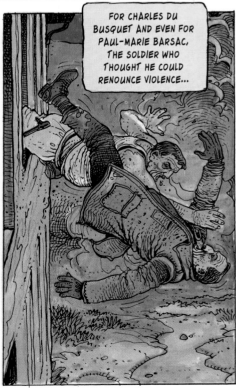

...HELL FOR ALFRED COLPIN AND FRANCISCO JAVIER...

AND FINALLY, HELL FOR CHRISTIAN AVIDSEN...

GET IN! WITH THE ARMS THEY'VE GOT STORED IN THERE, IT'S ALL GOING TO BLOW!

AND WHAT DO YOU THINK YOU'RE DOING HERE?

OH, I JUST HADN'T LEFT YET, THAT'S ALL...

PENG

AAH!

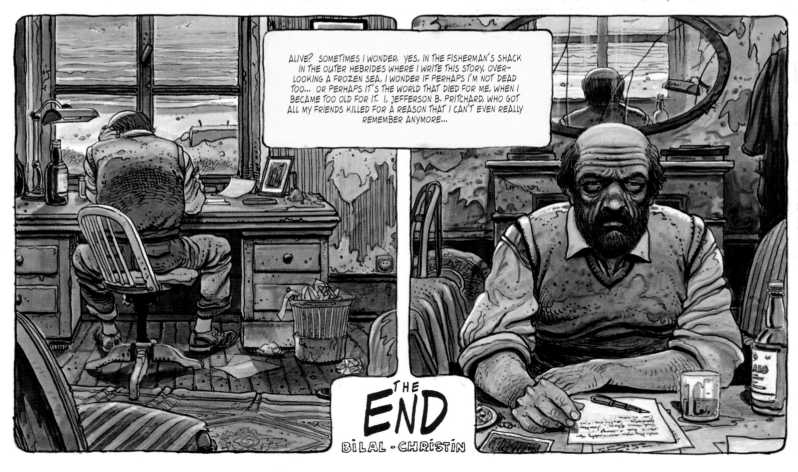

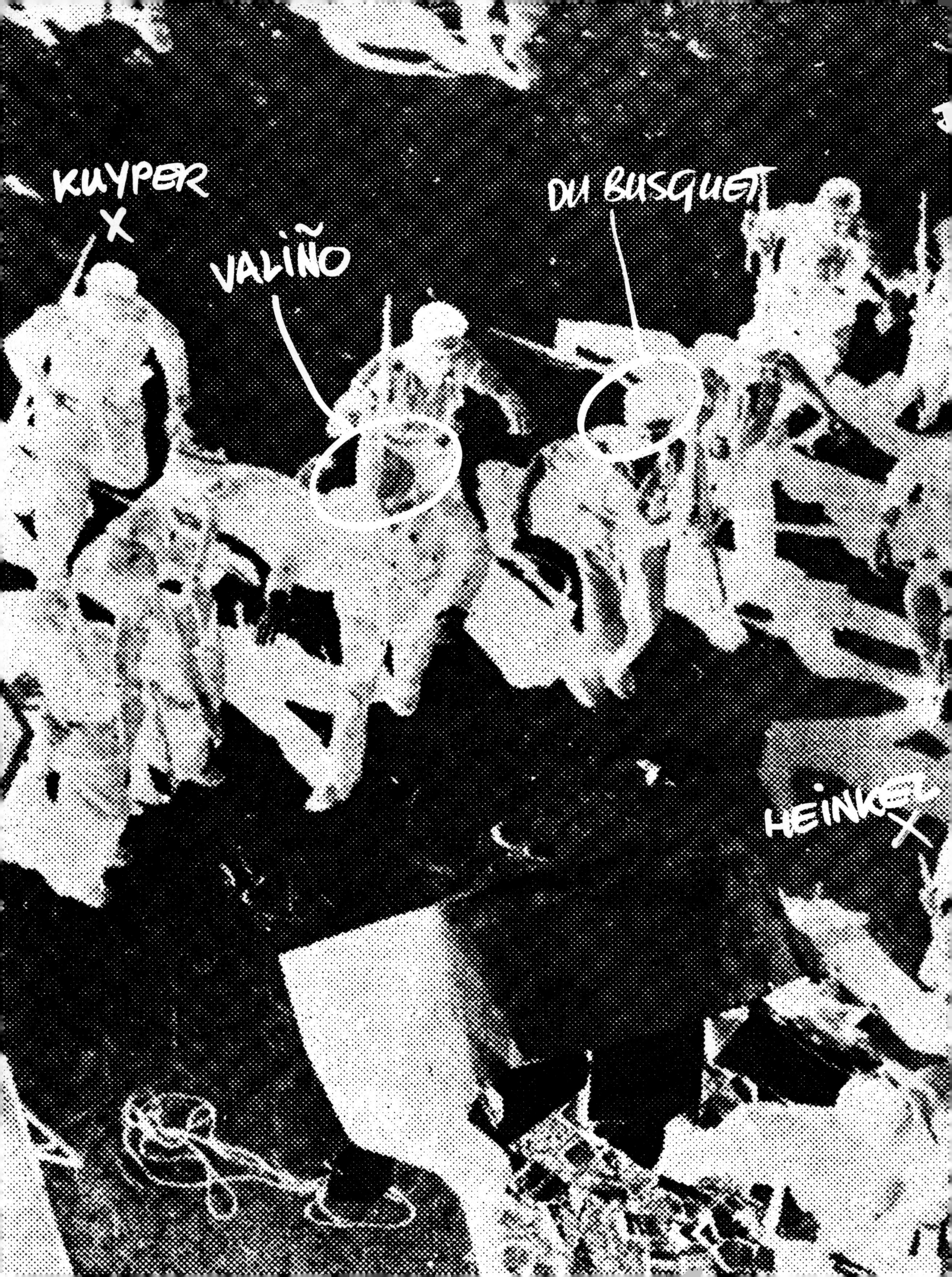
KUYPER
VALIÑO
DU BUSQUET
HEINKEL

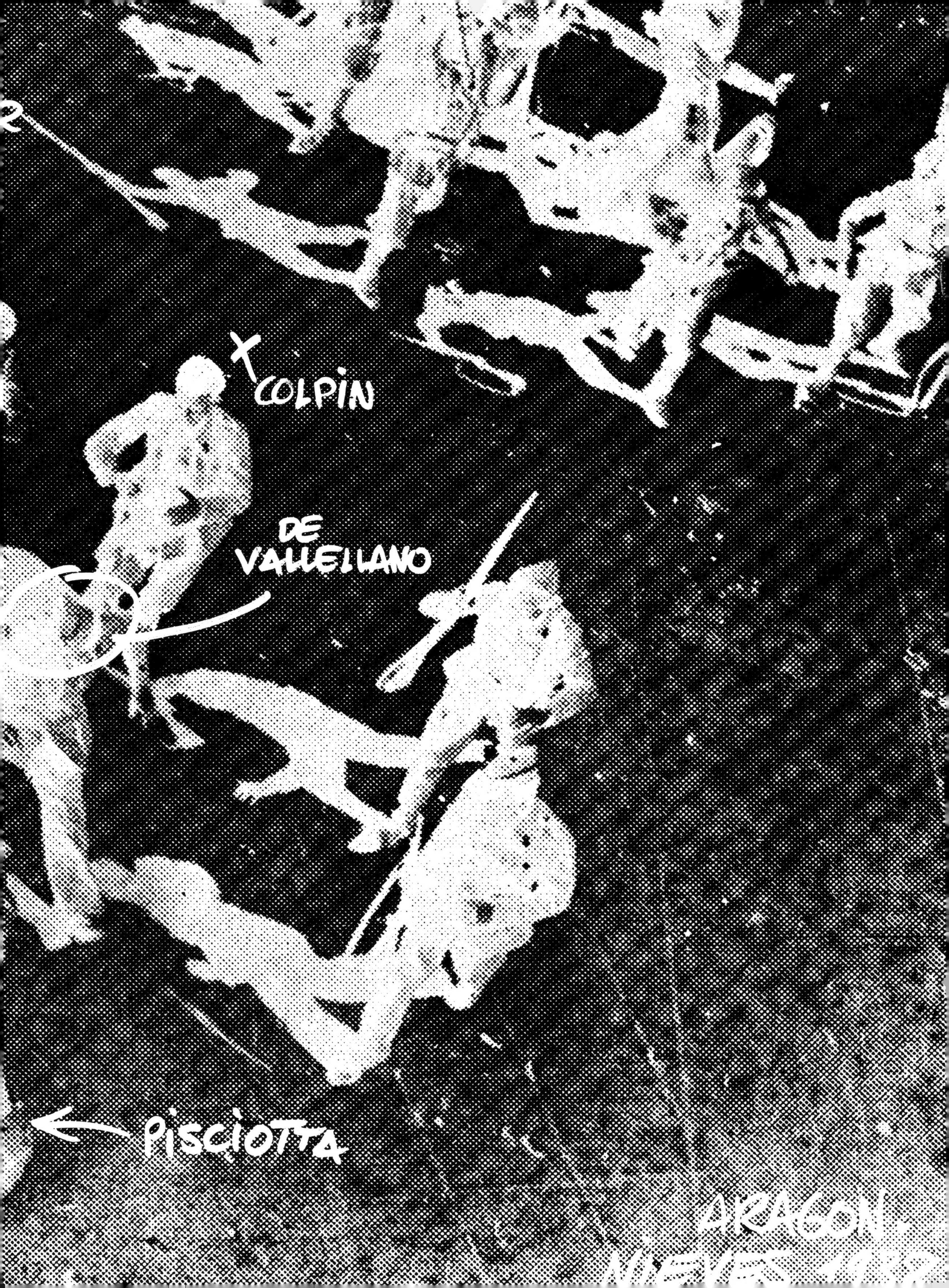
COLPIN
DE VALLELLANO
PISCIOTTA
ARAGON